Where is Hannah?

By Annette Smith

Illustrated by Priscilla Cutter

Hannah and Mom
went to the gym.

"Oh! Look, Mom!"
said Hannah.

"I can see a trampoline.

Look at the rope

and the ladders."

"Come and look at me, Mom!
I can go up and down
on the trampoline,"
said Hannah.
Hannah went up and down,
up and down, up and down.

"Look at me!
I'm on the rope,"
said Hannah.
"Come and look at me, Mom.
I can swing on the rope."

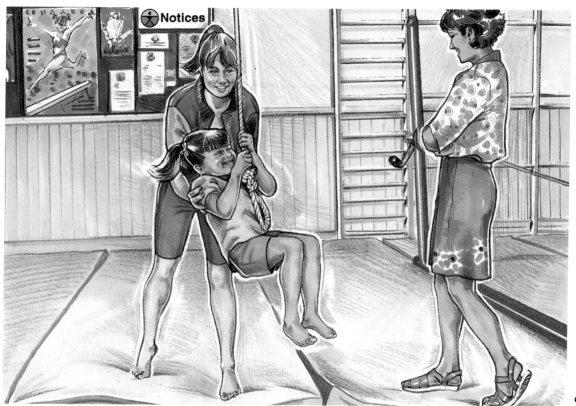

Mom went away
to look at the notices.

Hannah looked at the ladder.
"I can go up ladders,"
said Hannah.

Hannah went up the ladder.
She went up, and up, and up.

Mom looked for Hannah.
She looked at the rope.
She went to the trampoline.

"Hannah!

Hannah! Where are you?"

said Mom.

Hannah looked down at Mom.

"Here I am, Mom," shouted Hannah. "I'm way up here."